DOCKSIDE EXTRAS

STAGE **6** BOOK 3

SECRETS IN THE DARKNESS

John Townsend

RISING STARS

CHAPTER 1

The night filled with a terrible noise. Everyone in the West End Flats woke in an instant. A fire alarm was wailing. That meant only one thing — get out fast!

There was a mad scramble. At 02.16, people left their apartments to wait in the entrance. "Is it a real fire or a false alarm?" they said. No one knew.

But a figure on the stairs knew the truth.
He hid in the darkness.

CHAPTER 2

The Night Before

"There's something odd going on," Lee told Roo. "I can hear voices in Flat 51. It's been empty for years. Is it possible someone has moved in and ..."

Roo spoke before Lee could finish her sentence. "It must be the plumber or gas man. They're still doing improvements to the kitchen. When I asked them who's moving in, they wouldn't tell me. It's top secret."

Lee went on, "Mum said she saw men taking in boxes of stuff. She saw one of those horrible stripy paintings that Oz likes. I hope we don't get odd people moving in. We don't want rowdy students who party and dance all night."

"Or a violent nutter!" Roo gave a scary chuckle.

Lee grabbed a pillow and threw it at him. "Stop trying to scare me!" she giggled.

CHAPTER 3

Gran Val burst through the door. "I've been talking to Lee and Roo," she said. "They told me about Flat 51. Roo isn't sensible and Lee isn't reliable so I went to look for myself. I have seen the evidence. Men are fitting kitchen equipment. I asked them who is moving in and when. They said *no comment*."

Gran Val continued, "I told them I'm a resident of these flats and I want to know. They told me it was none of my business. What madness! Goodness knows why they won't tell me. As if telling me will make any difference."

"Yes it will, Gran. You'll tell the whole world," Jack added. "I saw the men take up a drum kit. Maybe a rock star is moving in. That would be unbelievable and brilliant. I can't wait to find out who it is."

Gran began to whisper as if she had the biggest secret, "I'll tell you something. I saw a food delivery van. That means they're moving in at any moment. I shall pop up in advance and leave a little present and card. I think it's important to be friendly."

Jack grinned cheekily, "I never knew you could be pleasant, Gran. I thought you just had a weakness for being nosy."

She grabbed a pillow and threw it at him.

"That's more like you — violence!" he laughed.

No one opened the door at Flat 51. "I know someone's in there," Gran Val snapped. "I've rung the bell and knocked."

"Maybe they just want to be left alone," Roo said.

"Maybe they can't speak English," Lee whispered.

"I know how to find out who lives here," Jack grinned. "Leave it with me!"

CHAPTER 4

At 02.15, Jack crept upstairs. He stood on the landing a short distance from Flat 51 and waited in silence. The secret would soon be over. The new resident would have to come out and be seen.

Jack hit the fire alarm. It was no accident.
The night filled with a terrible noise.

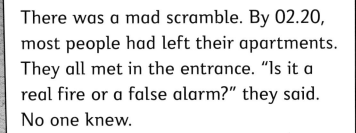

There was a mad scramble. By 02.20, most people had left their apartments. They all met in the entrance. "Is it a real fire or a false alarm?" they said. No one knew.

Then Jack ran in. "They're coming," he shouted.
"I ran down different stairs but they're on their way. You won't believe it. It's unbelievable!"

At that moment, Oz appeared. "Hi," he said calmly. "Nadia and I live here. Meet my new adorable wife. She's the lovable Nadia!"

They all stared in amazement
... and cheered.

1. What was the terrible noise in the night?

2. At what time did people leave their apartments?

3. Lee heard voices from an empty flat. Which one?

4. What had Gran Val seen at the same flat?

5. What was Jack's plan?

6. Who came out of the mystery flat?

7. What was their secret?

*Find the **verbs** to fill the gaps.*

1. A fire alarm was _____.   (page 2)

2. She saw men _____ in boxes of stuff.   (page 6)

3. Men are _____ kitchen equipment.   (page 8)

What's missing?

1. i know someones in there gran val snapped
   (page 14)

2. is it a real fire or a false alarm they said   (page 19)

3. theyre coming he shouted   (page 19)

*Find the **nouns** to fill the gaps.*

1. A figure on the _____ knew the truth.   (page 2)

2. I can hear _____ in Flat 51.   (page 4)

3. She saw men taking in _____ of stuff.   (page 6)

4. By 02.20, most people had left their _____ .
   (page 19)

Which word in the story means

1. awful or dreadful?   (page 2)

2. loud or noisy?   (page 6)

3. proof?   (page 8)

4. a gift?   (page 12)

*Swap the word in **bold** for a new word that means the opposite.*

5. Roo spoke before Lee could **finish** her sentence.

6. Gran began to **whisper**.

7. I never knew you could be **pleasant**.

8. No one **opened** the door.